FOLK TALES
FROM THE
LAND'S END

William Bottrell

GW00391695

TOR MARK PRESS · REDRUTH

THE TOR MARK SERIES

FOLKLORE

OTHER TITLES

The cover illustration is by Tony Morris

First published 1998 by Tor Mark Press
United Downs Industrial Estate, St Day, Redruth, Cornwall, TR16 5HY
© Tor Mark Press 1998
ISBN 0-85025-366-7
Printed in Great Britain by Cornwall Lithographic Printers Ltd, Redruth

The giants of Castle Treen

The earliest inhabitants of this stronghold (which you will find called on modern maps Treryn Dinas) were giants who protected the neighbouring people in return for cattle and other necessaries, as was usual here in olden times.

An aged giant, his childless wife, and their adopted son are the only ones of whom traditions are handed down by the old folks of Treen. Not only this giant and his wife, but all people who depended on his protection in Treen and neighbouring places, were much grieved and disappointed when they found their giant and giantess were middle-aged and had no children who would aid them in old age and perpetuate the race.

The giantess, having no household to think about, grew, as most unemployed women do, peevish and troublesome. The giant, having little or no work to occupy himself with, grew fat and lazy. Quiet and good-tempered as he was, he was dreadfully tormented by his wife. She called him a lazy, useless old loon, and said he was too fat, and didn't take enough exercise. When he had nothing else to employ himself about, in peaceful times, she told him that he should log the rock for a few hours every day, to stretch his sinews and make the blood circulate brisker, instead of dozing away all day and night in his chair – which may still be seen.

'Go thee way'st,' said she; 'swim over to the Dollar Rocks, it's only two miles or so. Dive round them and catch me a few good big congers; I want their fat to make a cake. And the pollock and cod that feed among the ore-weed thereabouts are excellent eating.'

The dissatisfied woman's advice was sometimes taken. He would swim away and in an hour or two bring her home a string of fish of a furlong's length.

Then he would log Men Amber for a bit. This he could easily do with the tip of his finger, when standing on the grass below it, for the rock is only thirty feet or so from the grass and Treen giant stood at least forty feet high without his boots. He was stout in proportion and his strength of arm was prodigious. Sometimes, with his staff, he kept the sacred stone in motion when seated in his chair just opposite. But often it happened, when he exercised in this way, that he fell asleep long ere the sand was down in his wife's hour-glass. And then she, the faggot, would pelt her quiet husband with rocks, heaps of which may still be seen, lying loose just as they flew from her hand and dropped, at no great distance from the poor giant's chair. He would wake up, with a sore head, to hear her say in a voice like a bellowing bull, 'Stop thy snoring, thou confounded old fool, and work away, west ah? or I'll pommel thy noddel to browse.'

'What the deuce shall I do to stop her tongue and cure her temper? Can 'e tell me, my good people?' he would often say to Treen folks, and others who visited him on a summer's evening. 'She's the most troublesome woman I ever heard of.'

All kinds of employment were suggested. In those days every man thought he could manage a discontented wife, were he her husband; but actually to do it was more difficult.

'Why should she fret and fume for lack of children,' he used to say to his Treen neighbours, 'and what need do you have, either, in these peaceful times, to care whether we have descendants or not?'

Potent reasons were given both by giantess and people why they desired their chief's race should be continued. Charms and other means were used in order to obtain the desired result.

Yet much time passed and their rock-hewn cradle was still empty, when a happy thought struck a wise man of Treen. He advised that a baby should be stolen from the giant of Maen, who had a large family and was, moreover, a very troublesome and aggressive neighbour.

Our giant and his wife were delighted with the sage man's advice. To steal a baby from the big man, who was proud of his stronghold between Pen-von-las [Land's End] and Pedn-men-du, would be capital revenge on him and his. 'Then how nice it will be for me,' said the giant's wife, 'to sit on the Logan stone with the cheeld in my arms, of summer afternoons, when the waves sing lulla-bye and my old man can rock us till the dear baby falls asleep. Or he may dandle it in his arms atop of Castle Peak, or jump with it thence, from carn to carn, to Gamp-an-sees rock and back again, whilst I skin an ox for our supper; and you, my dear people, can bring us down plenty of milk to nurse him on, that he may grow apace.'

A wise woman, or witch, of Treen, who could take any shape, was selected as the most likely person to execute their project without causing any stir with the Maen giant, who was very fierce, and proud of his descent from blustering old Bellerus, who was said to have lived thereabouts in days of yore.

One afternoon, away went the witch, and without being noticed on the road she reached Cairn-men-ellas, where she hid herself between rocks to watch. A little before sunset she saw a giant's child, four years old or so, coming that way with some common people's children who wanted to show him how to play 'bob'. Now the infant giant, though nearly as big as an ordinary man, was still a baby in every feature and hadn't been long weaned; he still wore a bib, though he had outgrown his clothes, and his frock and save-all [pinafore] scarcely reached to his knees. The common boys and girls, from ten to a dozen years of age and like in size to him, led about the great 'slab' as they called him, and did with him just as they pleased.

The woman, seeing them place buttons (and they hadn't many) on the bob, took from her basket a string of large bright ones, shook them before the giant baby and said, 'Now kiss me, dear, and I will give 'e all these.' He kissed her again and again, delighted to have the buttons. Over awhile she said, 'The tides are low and I'm on my way to get lempots and gweans [limpets and winkles] from Cowloe. Will 'e go, dears?'

The elder ones said it was then too late – they must all be home to Treve before sundown, or their mammies would strap them soundly and send them to bed without supper. But the babe-giant said, 'I'll go, for I want some gweans to play five-stones, and lempots too, that my da may shoe the cats with croggans [limpet-shells] and codgey-wax [cobblers'-wax]. He do dearly like that fun and my ma do never beat me.'

'Come along then, my turtle,' said the witch, and she took his hand and led him off. On the way she took from her basket many toys, and showed him how to play with them. This pleased him, so that he thought no more of Cowloe, and she led him away over the Green to Brew Moors, where, to divert him, she changed herself into the shape of a horse and he trotted on her back a mile or more, when she resumed her woman's form. and led him into Castle Treen, where he was received with open arms by the mistress.

During his infancy he often reposed in a small chair that may still be seen near the large one in which the giant usually rested – the one just opposite the Logan Rock; and until he grew too big, he frequently slept in the giant's arms.

At sunrise in summer the old giant delighted to carry him up to Castle Peak, where he placed the infant to stand on the topmost stone, and name to him all the noted places within ken. After turning him round that he might behold the wild sea-lashed headlands in the distance, and noble carns towering near, he would exclaim, 'My dear boy, who wouldn't be proud of such a home as this? Believe me, my dear son, in all this western land, from the Lizard Point yonder to Pedn-penwith, which lies under the setting sun, there is not another giant who owns a place equal to Castle Treen; and all shall be thine, my darling, when I am dead and gone.'

When the sun shone warm, he took baby down to the Castle Leas, near the Gap. This was his favourite fishing place, where a deep pit may still be seen in which he pounded browse, that was cast on the water to entice in fish. From these rocks at the water's edge, the giant like a monstrous dolphin stretched on the sea, with the boy standing on his broad back and, holding on with both hands by the hair of his head like bridle-reins, would swim out and round to the Sees rock. Having rested there a while and given the cheeld a few shags' eggs, limpets, mussels and such like dainties, back they would steer, but farther out, and coasting all the seaboard of his Castle, land in Par Pry.

When he was a few years older, the giant taught his boy to fish from the rocks with rod and line, showed him how to make fish-hooks out of bones and croggan-rims – as boys out there do now, or did not long ago. In the time of the giants they hadn't a bit of iron, not even a nail.

It wasn't much, however, that the giant knew how to teach the youngster. Like all of great bulk, he had more strength than knowledge; as we say, 'the best goods are bound up in the smallest bundles.'

Meanwhile the giantess took care that the boy had an unlimited supply of food, that he might eat and drink whenever he chose. Over a few years he was nearly equal in bulk to his new Dadda, as he called the old giant.

We like to linger over these pleasant times for the old Titan, when he took much delight in his charge. But alas! the sequel must be told in tears and sorrow for female frailty. We don't like to repeat all the stories handed down, which for the most part are highly unfavourable to the moral character of the Treen giantess, yet we must say that all traditions represent her as a most abandoned female in her later years.

All her care and attention were bestowed on the boy and she neglected her old husband, so that he had to dive for fish and skin oxen. Sheep he could seldom get; they were dainties reserved for the young fellow. The poor old giant was often driven to such extremities that, to appease hunger which makes brutes of the best of men, he was fain to stay his stomach on ore-weed.

To add insult to injury she often taunted her aged spouse with his weakness, which was the consequence of her neglect, and cut him to the heart by making unfavourable comparisons between him and the pampered youth, who could now log the rock from sitting on the grass. And that was more, the giantess told her husband, than he could do at the height of his strength.

Worst of all, her maternal love then changed into a passion that, all things considered, one might even now in these days of lax morality and free-love [1873!] regard as reprehensible.

The poor old giant was slow to become jealous, till he found himself utterly forsaken by his spouse and adopted son, who always stole away to sunny glades between the carns to play by themselves. That would have passed without notice – he rather liked to be left alone to doze in his chair – had not some Treen women, who were sharp in such things, spied what was going on and out of envy told the old giant.

He then became very surly and gave the doting pair much annoyance by coming on them unawares when they withdrew to enjoy their amorous diversion. They had seldom much comfort then, except when the old fellow left the castle to get provision.

One winter's day, when he was about to start for this purpose, he told his wife and the youngster that one of them should meet him on his way back to assist in taking home whatever he might procure.

They promised to do so but time passed so pleasantly with the couple that they thought but little of their good old provider till they heard his footsteps and angry voice, about a quarter of a mile off, as he came stamping along Pedn-y-vounder cliff vowing vengeance on his ungrateful wife and foster-son.

They became somewhat frightened, and the giantess, knowing that, 'the first blow was half the battle', prepared for the encounter by placing herself on the rocks west of the Gap, a dozen feet or so above the narrow path which the giant would have to pass. He came stamping along, an ox on his shoulders, and on each arm he carried a sheep, basket fashion, their trotters bound with their spans.

He roared louder than the stormy breakers when he entered his castle's inner enclosure and found that no one, even then, came to meet him. In his fury he bounced along without noticing his wicked rib awaiting his approach, with her bared arm and clenched fist, and as he came along the narrow ledge she dealt him a blow in the eyes, as he glanced towards her, that sent him, cattle and all, heels over head down the precipice.

When she beheld him falling, a memory of their early loves, or something else, caused a sudden revulsion of feeling, which made her regret her rashness; unwilling to witness her husband's dying agony, she stepped back westward about twenty paces, onto a level stone between high rocks, where she stood still and cast her apron over her head that she might hear less of the giant's awful moans. Though the giant's skull was very thick, it was badly smashed on the boulders, yet he didn't die before he had called upon the Powers whom he served to avenge him, which they did instantly by changing his vile partner into stone, where she stood, and where she may still be seen. The old giant, in his dying moments, thought of the young one more in sorrow than in anger – he couldn't in his heart feel very bitter against the simple-innocent hobble-de-hoy, and regarded his wife as the seducer.

Of late the Giant's Lady, as she was formerly called, has been named the Logan Rock's Lady by those who are ignorant of our traditions. When tempests rage, or anything else excites her, she rocks to and fro, but her movements are languid with age and sorrow. Pitiless storms have so beaten on her head that one can't make out a feature, and her fair proportions are so mutilated that one can scarce discern a semblance of her gigantic form in the time-worn granite mass.

The giant of Carn Galva

This giant was more playful than warlike. Though the old works of the giant now stand desolate, we may still see, or get up and rock ourselves upon, the logan stone which this dear old giant placed on the most westerly carn of the range, that he might log himself to sleep when he saw the sun dip into the waves and sea-birds fly to their homes in the cleeves.

Near the giant's rocking seat one may still see a pile of cubical rocks which are almost as regular and shapely now as when the giant used to amuse himself in building them up, and kicking them down again, for exercise or play when alone and he had nothing else to do. People of the northern hills have always had a loving regard for the memory of this giant because he appears to have passed all his life at the carn in single blessedness, merely to protect his beloved people of Morvah and Zennor from the depredations of the less honest Titans who then dwelt on Lelant hills. Carn Galva giant never killed but one of the Morvah people in his life, and that happened all through loving play.

The giant was very fond of a fine young fellow of Chûn, who used to take a turn over to the carn every now and then, just to see how the old giant was getting on, to cheer him up a bit, play a game of bob, or anything else to help him pass his lonely time away. One afternoon the giant was so well pleased with the good play they had together that when the young fellow of Chûn threw down his quoit to go away home, the giant in a good natured way tapped his playfellow on the head with the tips of his fingers.

At the same time he said, 'Be sure to come again tomorrow, my son, and we'll have a capital game of bob.' Before the word 'bob' was well out of the giant's mouth, the young man dropped at his feet. The giant's fingers had gone right through his playmate's skull. When at last the giant became aware of the damage he had done to the young man's brain-pan, he did his best to put the inside workings of his mate's head to rights, and plugged up his finger holes, but all to no purpose; for the young man was stone dead and cold long before he ceased doctoring his head.

When the poor giant found it was all over with his playmate, he took the body in his arms and, sitting down on a large square rock at the foot of the carn, he rocked himself to and fro. Pressing the lifeless body to his bosom, he wailed and moaned over him, bellowing and crying louder than the booming billows breaking on the rocks in Permoina.

'Oh, my son, my son, why didn't they make the shell of thy noddle stronger? A es as plum [soft] as a piecrust, dough baked, and made too thin by half! How shall I ever pass my time without thee to play bob and mop-and-heede [hide and seek]?'

The giant of Carn Galva never rejoiced any more but, within seven years or so, he pined away and died of a broken heart.

The tragic I'ans of Treen

Some few years ago, there might have been seen on rising ground, west of the road which passes through Treen, the remains of a very old dwelling, formerly known in that neighbourhood as the I'an's house. Though neglected and ruinous it still retained some signs of its former consequence, when it was regarded as a mansion.

Three or four centuries ago, from their extravagance and a run of bad luck, the I'ans were reduced to comparative poverty. It was said that ill fortune ever followed them from the time they broke up and removed the Garrack Sans (holy rock) that stood in front of their mansion, and around which a market was held in old times when Treen was an important trading place. However that may have been, shortly after, all the family remaining in Treen were John I'an and his sister Beatrice, usually called Beaton, who had lost their parents when children. Young I'an, from having much family pride and but little property to support its dignity, led a very settled life – mostly at sea, with a company of reckless young men, who carried on a hazardous trade in importing liquors, silks, salt and other contraband goods from Roscoff; making Penberth, or some other cove near it, their usual landing place. Both brother and sister are said to have been remarkable for their tall stature and good looks, though of very dark complexion.

They might, now and then, be seen at church, John dressed in a long bottle-green coat of cut velvet and dusky crimson waistcoat (both overlaid with tarnished gold lace), plush breeches and diamond-buckled shoes. These everlasting garments, that might have been worn by his grandfather, were only changed in winter for home spun; and his sturdy legs were then encased in long funnel-topped boots of French make; and his jet black hair, that hung in curls on his shoulders, was surmounted by a laced hat and plume. Though young I'an's state dress appeared much the worse for wear, he looked every inch a gentleman when, with old-fashioned courtesy, he led into church his sister, arrayed in silks or samite a century old or more, yet still looking rich with their brilliant sheen, and thick enough to stand on end. Point-lace ruffles, yellow with age, hanging from her elbows, were met by embroidered silk gloves; her hair, of darkest chestnut hue, turned back over cushions, hung in ringlets down her neck, and a little hat was fastened by jewel-headed pins to her high head-dress. These remnants of old finery, contrasted with homely articles of dress that had to sustain more wear and tear, made the I'ans' poverty only too apparent; the more so because at that time several well-to-do families resided in St Levan, and at church their old bravery and newest fashions were all displayed and duly criticised. Beaton showed what her brother thought becoming pride, in treating with coolness or contempt all attentions offered by such rural beaux as he thought beneath her, though she had but slight chance, poor girl, of becoming acquainted with any of higher rank.

I'an being seldom at home during the summer, his sister and two or three old servants managed the farm – then but a few acres of arable land and a great run of common – and were sole occupants of their gloomy mansion.

The poor young lady's dreary existence was partly relieved by her brother's presence during the winter. Then too he often brought home with him many of his sea-mates or hunting companions and the old house resounded with their reckless drunken revelry for days and nights together.

Among I'an's comrades his favourite was an able seaman called Willy Taskes or Trevaskes, who was a few years older than I'an – a courageous smuggler and mate of his fair-trader the *Mur*. Taskes was remarkably strongly built, the best wrestler and boxer in the western parishes. With much practice he taught I'an these arts of self-defence, and trained him to be just as good a seaman as himself. I'an when overloaded with drink was often quarrelsome or rather fond of fighting without reason, both at home and abroad. Taskes as often belaboured him soundly to avert his combative inclinations from dangerous antagonists; often also he got himself thrashed black and blue in taking I'an's part, which he was ever ready to do against any odds. From Willy being frequently in Beaton's company, and from the favour shown him by her brother, she was less reserved with him than others of his crew whom she kept at due distance.

Of an evening when he often came alone, Beaton would ask him to card the wool that she passed great part of her time in spinning, and no one more willing than Willy Taskes to please her. I'an frequently left them together, little deeming that his sister – of gentle blood, poor as she might be – could have a thought of the handsome young sailor as a lover. Ere long, however, I'an was informed by his ugly old female domestic – one who ever longed for but never had a lover – that her young mistress often met Will Taskes by night in the walled garden, Caercreis barn, or among the Castle carns. I'an, enraged, entered his sister's apartments – she had three rooms at her sole disposal in that portion of the mansion known as Beaton's wing – and after much upbraiding threatened to shoot Taskes if he came near the house any more, and both of them if he caught them together. Beaton defied her brother and answered that if she could not see Willy Taskes there she would meet him elsewhere, and that it only depended on Will as to whether she would be his wife or not.

Warned of what had taken place, the lover kept aloof, and I'an, discarding his jovial companions, remained much within doors, moody and discontented, wishing for the company of his former comrades; but pride forbade his making friendly overtures and his ill humour was aggravated all the more because his sister had the policy to persuade him that, after all, she didn't care anything for Will Taskes nor any of his crew, and that his chagrin was all for nought. The dreary winter past, and corn tilled, I'an and his crew prepared for an early trip to Roscoff. Their former mate, from his quarrel with the captain, or rather from the coolness between them, having gone to work on land, they selected a new one and made sail.

I'an left on good terms with his sister, thinking that, though she might have had an unbecoming affection for Taskes, yet her self-respect and regard for the dignity of their family – which he had awakened – had enabled her to subdue her misplaced love.

In a few weeks the *Mur* returned with the usual goods, which were soon landed and disposed of, as the most valuable liquors, silks and laces were bespoke by the neighbouring gentry. Farmers and others who assisted to land and secure the cargo soon took off what remained. There was then little or no interference from any government officials; indeed in more recent times those paid to check 'fair-trade' were often the smugglers' friends, because they durst not interrupt their proceedings with anything but well understood shams of activity, and they were always rewarded with a share of the goods if they conducted themselves with discretion. Old smugglers say they often wished to fall in with the Revenue cutter that their trip might be the more exciting – they answered her shots by a loud hurrah and a blaze from their own swivel-gun.

All hands being ready for another trip, the evening before they intended to start I'an told his sister he was going to meet his crew at the 'Skaw Tree' – the inn at St Levan Churchtown – have a carouse and sail in the morning early. Wishing to become friends with his old mate, I'an had requested one of his crew to tell Taskes that he would be glad of his company at the public house and to let all past unpleasantness be forgotten. In I'an's happier moods a lingering regard for his former comrade and staunch friend would get the upper hand of his prejudice and family pride, and then he would think of Taskes as his brother-in-law with complacency.

From jealousy on the part of the new mate and others, his friendly message was not delivered. I'an, not guessing the reason why Taskes didn't join them and only thinking his offers of renewed friendship were slighted, was in ill humour. What was intended to have been a jovial night passed unpleasantly. At length some of the fuddled crew, vexed because of their captain's preference for his former mate, hinted that he might be at Caercreis barn, in company he better liked, and that by all accounts his sister and Willy had always been on very good terms. I'an, tipsy as he was, understood their meaning, made imprudent threats of the way he would be revenged on Taskes, and left the company much earlier than was his wont on such occasions.

Very mixed feelings, and all of an irritating nature, spurred him on his way towards an old solitary bowjey [field barn] where a cottage now stands, five minutes from Castle Treen; and he had only gone a few yards beyond Pedn-y-vounder lane when, by the dim moonlight, he spied two persons sauntering along a sheep track that wound among rocks and carns below him. Approaching and seeing they were his sister and her lover he assailed them with angry words, which soon came to blows between the men. Taskes, finding I'an was the worse for drink, merely defended himself and received the blows, that he might expend his fury upon him, as he had often done when they were the best of friends. But as bad luck would have it, Taskes, in going back to avoid what might have been ugly strokes, fell over a rock onto a shelf many feet below.

When I'an saw the young man he had once loved as a brother lying prostrate and apparently dead, his pride and anger gave place to bitter sorrow. He raised the wounded man, who moaned and gasped for breath for some minutes; then, hearing I'an crying like a child, begging him to forget and forgive the past and be friends, Taskes replied

'I have nothing to forgive thee, my son. It was my bad luck and, whether I die or live a cripple, I would rather for it to be my case than thine.'

Over a while, I'an and his sister helped him to stand, and one on either side of him, with his arm round the neck of each, they slowly reached their house and placed him on I'an's bed. The servant-man was summoned and told to ride with all speed for a doctor. Taskes tried to speak and signed that he might be lifted up in bed. Supported on I'an's breast, and holding the brother's and sister's hands, he said, 'I know, dear John, a doctor can do me no good.' And looking toward Beaton he told her to bring the servant close to the bedside, for he had something to say before it might be too late.

The old man approached. Taskes called him by name and continued, 'I am dying. None but ourselves know how I came by my end. You must bear witness for John your master that I declare it was all by my own mischance that I fell over a rock and received my deadly hurt.' He hadn't the strength to say more. I'an wiped the bloody froth from the sinking man's lips and tried to cheer him by saying, 'Thou shalt live yet, my dear Willy, and be my brother.'

Beaton, like one in a terrible dream was unconscious of most that passed, till Taskes, awakening from a long swoon, grasped her hand and moaned in sad accents, 'Beaton, dear Beaton, if I could but live till we might be married, I should die more content. And my dear John,' he continued, directing his gaze towards I'an, 'promise me, for all the years we have been like brothers, to be ever kind to Beaton and to my – our – ' He gasped for breath, with a gurgling in his throat, blood oozed from his lips. Looking wistfully at Beaton he grasped brother's and sister's joined hands with a death-grip; his head sunk on I'an's breast; and thus Willy Taskes passed away in his prime.

Beaton, distracted by sorrow, had to be forcibly taken from her lover's bedside and for weeks she seemed to be on the verge of madness. Her brother scarcely less grieved, tried to find some solace for his anguish in ordering that in all respects the funeral should be conducted as for one of his kindred. It was a custom with the I'ans, and a few other West Country families, to have their burials at night. So, a week after the fatal encounter and in the summer evening's twilight, Willy Taskes was borne out of the old mansion, carried by his former comrades, followed by I'an and by many neighbours to his last resting place in St Levan churchyard.

I'an being reluctant to leave his sister all alone with her sorrow, procured a good seaman to command the *Mur* for her next run. Fears were entertained that Beaton's mind might become permanently deranged from excessive grief. She could seldom be induced to leave the room in which her lover had died, and, since I'an felt a repugnance to sleep there, she took it for a bedroom, saying she intended to keep it because that apartment, with two or three others adjoining it, were bequeathed to her (as indeed they were, with their furniture) for her lifetime. For many days together she was not seen except by the aged servant who, at the usual meal-times, took to the gloomy chamber food that was often removed untasted. Her spinning-wheel was thrown aside; yet she seemed occupied in some quiet mysterious way; and I'an, getting alarmed for the probable result of her sad seclusion, consulted a doctor, who, being an old friend of the family, came to visit Beaton without delay and requested to be taken to her room without being announced. I'an entered, followed by the doctor, and saw Beaton in a window-recess, busily sewing; at the same time, so absorbed was she in singing a baby's lullaby and rocking a cradle – in which there was no child, but a christening dress, with other articles of an infantile wardrobe – that she did not perceive her visitors. They noted, too, that the bed was covered with old dresses in various beautiful fabrics, and that Beaton had been cutting them up, seemingly to waste. I'an, annoyed to see this destruction of gay and costly gowns, said, 'Sister dear, art thou going crazy to be cutting up thy best clothes?'

'No John,' she replied, without looking up from her work, 'yet methinks you are very rude thus to enter a lady's bedchamber with so little ceremony. But men understand so little of women's hearts,' she continued, as if speaking to herself and taking no further notice of her brother. 'Little do they know that, when damsels don their gayest robes, they long for the time when they may cut them up for their babies' clothes. But is it tomorrow that is to be my wedding day?' she demanded. 'Oh, dear Willy, where art thou? Do tell me. It was to have been some time before brother John came back. The banns called thrice, we are to be wedded before he returns; then he will love my Willy like he used to, and all will be right well.'

Unconscious, seemingly, of any presence save what her crazed fancy imaged, she looked towards her brother and the doctor, who now advanced and noticed there was no intelligence in her fixed gaze. She appeared to be looking within rather than at anything external, when she went on to say, 'Our child, if a boy, shall be named William, after you my love, but if a girl it shall never be named Beatrice for me. I have often been told that the name, though a favourite one, has always been ill-starred in our family. Shall we call her Mary, for your mother, or Agnes, for mine? Any names of those we love sound sweet, like a dear mother's. That I remember, and how she rocked me singing, "Lullaby, lullaby, little maid Beatrice; angels protect thee, my darling."'

I'an, cut to the heart to see her thus, took her hand and said, 'Sister, you are ill, dear, and our good friend the doctor is come to visit you.' 'Oh, how foolish people are,' she replied, 'I was never better in my life, yet our old Betty will have it that I don't eat enough; what next I wonder? I am glad, however, he is come to visit us; our house seems lonely now, and he is a dear man – so kind, true, and hearty, I always liked him from a child, and how he enjoys his pipe and glass, dear man!'

Beaton folded her work, rose, passed near their friend without recognition, and descended to the kitchen, where she gave orders for a sumptuous repast, thought there was nothing in her house to furnish it. She then returned to her work, saying that it would be time enough to dress for dinner in an hour or more, meanwhile her brother would entertain their guest, and the doctor would excuse her, for indeed she was very busy.

The doctor, perceiving her pitiably distracted state, advised I'an to remove her to a change of scene – far away if he could – and trust to an occurrence that might soon take place to do more to restore her reason than anything in his power. 'Nature,' he observed, 'beats all doctors, and maternal instinct supplies the place of reason, now happily dormant for the assuagement of her bleeding heart, poor dove.'

The old servant being called and questioned, she confirmed what the doctor surmised, and further informed him that she was aware of the intention of William and Beaton to be married during her master's absence, trusting to have his forgiveness when all was done.

The doctor's advice tallied with I'an's inclination. He had often thought, and at length determined, to leave the wreck of his property for his creditors, as it was deeply mortgaged and the accumulated interest of many years unpaid. He would seek a home for himself and his sister in Brittany, where he had formed acquaintances, and where no fancied requirements of sham gentility and beggarly state would impede his endeavours to push his fortune by land or sea.

Being assured that a trip across the Channel was likely to prove beneficial to Beaton, who had often been to sea and enjoyed life on the waves, wearing apparel, bedding and a few heirlooms of no great value were packed so that they might be ready to leave when the *Mur* next made sail for France. Their movable furniture was placed in Beaton's part of the house, where two old servants were installed to keep possession for her of that, and also of some garden ground and pastureland in which she had a life interest.

It was feared there might be some difficulty in persuading the poor demented woman to embark; yet, when the vessel was ready, she was led by a harmless deception to connect the proposed voyage somehow with going to meet her lover and hastening to her bridal.. So, one day about a month after Willy was laid beneath the turf, I'an had a stone placed to mark the spot and – following a very ancient custom in St Levan – planted rosemary, box, lilies and other garden flowers on the grave, over which he and his crew shed many tears. The following night, I'an with his sister bade farewell to the ancient home of their forefathers, now rendered doubly sad to him by the remembrance of Taskes' ill-fated death and his sister's melancholy plight.

Little more was then heard of either brother or sister. Penberth men, belonging to I'an's crew, purchased his share of their vessel, and before they left port Beaton was lodged at a farmhouse, where she was kindly nursed. It was hoped that ere long maternal cares might tend to restore her reason and somewhat relieve her anguish for her lover's untimely death. I'an was well known at the port, where they had long traded, as an expert seaman and good navigator, and he soon obtained the command of a ship.

For a long while the old servants lived in Beaton's part of the house, hoping for her return, and cultivated the small quantity of ground that belonged to her. But no tidings ever reached them of either sister or brother; and when the two old servants died, it being supposed that their mistress was also dead and her portion reverted to I'an's estate, his creditors took possession of it.

Beaton's return

A little above Penberth Cove, and near the Green, there is an ancient cottage in an orchard. In this dwelling lived an old dame named Joan Taskes, who kept a kind of public house, as liquors and other goods were entrusted to her by smugglers for sale.

One afternoon, about twenty years after Willy's death, when he and the I'ans were almost forgotten, An' Joan, whilst busy spinning flax with a treadle turn, heard a knock at her open door; thinking it was somebody come to buy liquor or 'honey-pins' – a sweet apple for which her orchard was noted – without rising she called out, 'Come 'e in cheeld, and don't 'e stay knacking at the door.' But An' Joan was rather startled when, on looking round, she saw two ladies standing near her. They were both tall. One appeared about fifty and the other about twenty years of age. Their dresses made her think they must be foreigners. The elder was clad in some kind of white woollen stuff, by whatever name one might call her garb: it had loose hanging sleeves, and its ample folds were confined by a girdle to her waist. Over her head she wore a square of black serge; its ends, hanging on her shoulders and shading her face, gave it a pallid appearance, which was rendered somewhat ghastly by a white linen band across her forehead. The younger wore a silver-grey dress of more ordinary mode, and for head-dress a lace veil that covered, without concealing, her braided dark brown hair.

An' Joan, rising, said, 'Pray be seated, ladies, and excuse me, as I thought you might have been some neighbours' children knocking at the door.'

'We called,' the elder lady replied, to enquire if there be any small dwelling unoccupied in Penberth, or Treen, or in any place near.'

'Be blessed to sit, ladies, and leave me think a moment,' said the dame, 'but I haven't heard of any place that would be good enough for you, and the only one I know of, close at hand, is Chynance. Why, it seems to me,' she continued, as if I had heard the sound of your voice, years ago, somewhere, but can't call 'e to mind.'

'Look at me well, Aunt Joan,' the lady rejoined, 'and tell me if you can think of anyone you ever saw like me.'

The dame adjusted her barnacles, peered at the lady's face and at length said in tremulous tones, 'You can't be a spirit, to come here high by day! Yet now I look at 'e again there's the dark brown eyes, straight nose, small mouth and pitted chin of our poor lost Beatie! You can't be she? But with that white band across your forehead one can't see a lock of your hair; hers was of the darkest chestnut colour; besides the black kerchief over your head shades your face.'

'If you saw my hair, now nearly as white as your own, you wouldn't know me by that,' the lady answered. 'But don't be frightened, dear An' Joan,' she continued, folding back her veil. 'Look again and you will see Beatrice I'an, and this dear girl is my daughter Mary.'

An' Joan sprung from her seat, kissed Mary, clasped Beaton to her breast and wept aloud for joy. She then took from her cupboard a bottle of brandy and another of mead, filled two rummers with a mixture of the strong and the sweet, saying, 'Here dears, drink this, and help yourselves to more while I get something for 'e to eat before I hear another word.'

The old dame skipped about as if the sight of Beaton and her daughter had made her twenty years younger.

In a few minutes An' Joan fried fish, boiled eggs, and placed on the board milk, cream and butter, with bread and honey, apple pasties, a jug of beer, and more bottles of her choice cordials. When all three had done ample justice to the repast, Beaton, looking round the dwelling, said, 'Now, Aunt Joan, I am again at home and as happy as I can ever hope to be, but I always felt like one banished for all the years I dwelt in the land where Mary was born and bred. Everything here looks the same as long ago, when my delight was to run down for some of your choice fruit and sweet flowers, and to play with your turn till you learnt me to spin just as well as yourself.'

'I hope, dears, you are now come home to live for the rest of your days,' said Joan. 'Your grand old house is cut to pieces, and three families dwelling in it; but most of your furniture is still there, packed away in the best chamber, with all in that room as you left it, and the door hasn't been unlocked for many years – scarcely opened indeed since you last slept there.'

Beaton replied that during all the time she lived abroad, her greatest desire was to return and end her days where she was born, and to be buried beside the one she loved above all the world; and that she intended, after a short rest, to go along the cliff to Church-town to see his grave, and that she wished to go alone.

'Poor dear Willy, the Lord rest with him,' said An' Joan, 'you will see by his grave that he hasn't been forgotten. On his breast there's a rosemary, the pride of my heart, grown to a bush that overtops his tombstone; a box tree grows at the foot, and betwixt them sweet-brier, tansy, herb-of-grace, and such other long-lived plants as are good for remembrance, besides a border of pinks and lilies. You'll see that none in the church-hay have been more lovingly tended, for I and others have planted on his grave fresh flowers when old ones died.'

When Cribba Head threw its shadow over the water, Beaton started on her sad pilgrimage, saying to her daughter, who wished to accompany her, 'Remain, dear, with our old friend; tell her all about your uncle John, and how we lived in Brittany; she is longing to know but don't like to ask.'

The kind dame took Mary round her garden, well stocked with sweet old-fashioned flowers and many hives of bees. Milking time being come, Joan took her bucket and they went up to Penberth Green, where the old dame's cow was waiting to be milked. At that time, and long after, almost every cotter kept a cow, which found sufficient pasture in green lanes and commons. An' Joan, having finished her outdoor evening work, made a mullet and parsley pie, as that was a favourite supper dish. When she had placed it on the hearth to bake, she said, 'I have for many years been longing to know how it fared with your mother and uncle, and had given up all hopes of ever seeing them, not knowing if they were alive or dead; and you, poor lonely flower, have no other relations on your mother's side that I know of.'

'I have many good cousins in Brittany,' replied Mary, 'as my uncle has a large family.' She then related what she had heard from her mother, and what she remembered, to the effect that when I'an settled in Brittany he hired a small farm, and soon after married a person of good property. For a short time he cultivated the land acquired by his marriage, but he soon tired of a farmer's life and went to sea as captain of a large ship; he was often away for years together. Mary seldom saw him, as there appeared to be little desire on the part of brother or sister for such intimacy. Yet on his return from a voyage, he always sent them money and goods, which they didn't require, because Beaton by her spinning and Mary by her lace-work and embroidery gained more than sufficed for their needs. Her uncle often took her lace-work abroad, where he traded, and brought her more for it than its weight in gold.

Although they wanted for nothing, and everybody was kind to them, Beaton was always pining to return. In spite of I'an's wishes for them to remain, she made a vow that before Mary became of age she would go home and pass the rest of her life in the practice of some devotion for the repose of Mary's father. About a week ago Beaton, having heard there was a smuggling craft from Cornwall in a cove near their dwelling, packed up all her household goods that she cared about and they left, bag and baggage, in the boat which landed them in Mousal that morning. When Mary had just ended her recital, her mother silently glided in, kissed her, and placed in her bosom a few flowers, saying, 'Cherish these, from a garden I prize above all others, and we will soon plant it with choicest flowers.

'And now,' she continued, 'we must bid dear Aunt Joan good-bye and proceed to Buryan Church-town where we can remain for the night.' 'No, my dears,' An' Joan interposed, 'there's a pie baking for your supper, and a spare bed on the talfat as good as any in Church-town, though I say it. Remain with me till you have found a better place, or hired Chynance for a time, as there may be more delay than you calculate before your house in Treen will be ready for 'e.' Both ladies gladly accepted the old dame's hearty welcome, and enjoyed her savoury pie and good ale of her own brewing; no woman then expected to get a husband unless she knew how to make a good barley-brew, and they say that people of that day, who drank good beer as their ordinary beverage, were stronger by far than their descendants raised on tea-wash.

Beaton hired Chynance, procured a few items of furniture, also a cow and poultry, had the garden planted, the house thatched and comfortably arranged for winter. Due to delay in getting possession of Beaton's property in Treen, they lived here a year or more. When all was ready for their removal, Mary would much have preferred to remain in that sunny sheltered cot, nestled at the foot of Buryan Hill; but her mother got into a restless fidgety state that caused An' Joan to look more grave than was her wont. She had heard that as far back as there was any record, many of the I'an family – particularly the women – when between forty-five and fifty went mad or died; she feared that the gloomy grandeur of Beaton's old home, with the sad remembrances, would tend to bring on this family infirmity. It was all in vain for Mary to say, 'Dear mother, let us remain here in this sunny nook, where flowers grow all the year, spotted trout sport in the stream, and our goats, lambs and poultry can range freely.'

When all was arranged in Beaton's part of the mansion, so as to give it an air of its former state, thither they moved – but retained Chynance for the sake of having pasture for their cow, and to please Mary.

Beaton was not in her old habitation many days before she had her turn and other spinning utensils taken into the chamber where Taskes breathed his last. There she passed most of her time, and often kept all night at her work; the rumble of her spinning wheels and doleful noises that she frequently made soon caused those living in the parts of the house not in her possession to quit, rather than have their rest nightly disturbed; and she rejoiced that the house was cleared of all strangers and interlopers, as she styled its other occupants.

On dark stormy nights she would often be met wandering along the cliffs between Church-town and Treen, or be seen kneeling on the rock where her lover received his fatal hurt, in her strange dress of white robe, black veil and ghastly linen band across her forehead, that made her look like one escaped from a grave in her winding sheet and shroud. It was evident that Beaton was at times insane; yet, sad as such a state seems, it may not have been the most melancholy portion of this poor soul's destiny. For when her mind was burthened with more grief than it could bear, her reason became unsettled and her memory infolded with clouds that were often of roseate hue.

As Penberth and Mousal fair-traders maintained a constant intercourse with Roscoff, I'an's family often sent Beaton presents of flax, clothing and other goods. They did not require them, however, for Mary like her mother was an excellent spinster and skilful in embroidery and lace-work. When Mary showed her rare lace to An' Joan, she assured her that ladies, within a short distance, paid large sums to smugglers for what was no better. The old dame took it round to gentlemen's seats and soon returned with much more money than Mary expected for her wares, and with orders for more lacework than she could execute in a long time.

Beaton's lucid intervals became less and less frequent. One of her strange freaks was to sleep by day and to visit the churchyard or spin by night. Sometimes she knitted stockings or other things for her Willy; these were to be put in her coffin. She would often say, 'Willy, dear, I am working for thee, my love, and will soon fetch thee back; we will live here, no one shall ever put us out of this chamber. Oh what delight I took in spinning years ago, when thou didst card the wool of winter's nights! And as of old thou shalt give me a kiss, such a long sweet kiss, with every rull I take from the cards.'

Her last whim was to spin and knit herself a shroud, which she called her wedding dress. The following night, she walked alone to the churchyard, and returned late.

About midnight Mary, as was her custom, looked into her mother's room and saw by the glimmering light of a chill [oil lamp] her mother sitting in a high-backed chair, apparently in a sweet sleep, with a placid smile on her countenance. Mary, loath to disturb her, stepped quietly back to her own room; but feeling uneasy from her mother's silence she lay awake till daybreak and then returned to her mother. On approaching her, Mary noticed that over a fine white dress she wore her shroud, with its face-cloth turned back on her head. Mary took her hand, and feeling it cold and stiff the truth struck her that her mother was dead. A neighbour, who was called in, assured Mary that her mother had been dead some hours. 'Yet to behold her thus, one would think she had only fallen asleep whilst saying her prayers, the Lord rest her poor soul.'

On looking round, when the rising sun-beams streamed in through an open window, they saw that her best quilt was spread on the bed, and on that the clothes Taskes wore on that unlucky night when he received his death wound, and other things that had belonged to him. Where or how Beaton could have kept them so long, no one knew. An' Joan had these, and withered flowers, with other things that Beaton prized, put into her coffin, in hopes to give her spirit rest; and Beatrice I'an, according to her oft-repeated request, was laid in St Levan churchyard beside the dust of Will Taskes.

'And we Treen people,' said the old man who related her story, 'would have been glad if she had stayed there, but she hadn't been under the turf three days when she was back again and spinning, as she always said she would; and it was supposed that other spirits came with her, from the capperouse they made.'

But we will leave those ghostly doings, which are described in another book in this series, *Classic Ghost Stories from the Land's End*, and turn instead to poor Mary's destiny.

Mary I'an and the Pendars

Mary's life had been anything but a cheerful one for the past year or two, but after her mother's decease she felt very desolate. Her uncle's family urged her to return and live with them, which she was inclined to do, as she often said that Brittany seemed less gloomy to her than this country; because in the Cornouaille over the water young and old met, every Sunday at least, and joined in a dance after service; besides, there were yearly feasts in neighbouring parishes on their patron saints' days, to which people flocked from miles away. They were hospitably entertained without regard to rank at the feasten board, and all regarded it as a sort of religious duty to take part in dancing, hurling, wrestling and other games that were continued several days of the feasten week.

'It seems to me like forsaking my poor mother to leave this place,' Mary would say to An' Joan, 'but over sea my cousins are always happy together, and they know no difference between me and their sisters; but here I feel as desolate as a forsaken bird, though Chynance is a pleasant sunny spot and nobody can be kinder to me than you and others who knew my poor dear mother.' In suchlike sad complaints she bemoaned her lonely state, till love came to brighten the scene, for a brief space.

Mary frequently took her work to Penberth and passed the afternoons or evenings with An' Joan. As the dame sold liquor from a noggin to an anker [keg] her dwelling was often pretty well filled with company of an evening. And Mary often said that such gatherings of neighbours, to hear news, sing songs or relate old stories, reminded her of home, as she called Brittany.

Now it soon happened, a few months after Mary again settled in Chynance, she was one afternoon on a visit to An' Joan when a young officer, home on furlough from a man-of-war, entered the dwelling, saluted An' Joan – who had known him from a child – and called for brandy and cordials to treat the dame and himself; by the time they were seated for a cosy chat, Mary entered with baskets of fruit from the orchard. The young sailor rose, saluted her, and seemed surprised to see one – apparently an inmate of Joan's – with the dress and demeanour of a lady; her broken English, with Breton accent, betokened her to be a foreigner. 'Don't 'e disturb yourself, Mr Pendar,' said An' Joan, 'this young lady, poor dear, all the same to me as a daughter, is the damsel Mary I'an.'

Mr Pendar had heard some gossip, on his first arrival at home, about the good looks, rare accomplishments and strange history of this waif of the I'ans; and how she had refused many offers of marriage from farmers' sons that were thought good chances for her. Young Pendar took a liking at first sight to the poor orphan, and his love was not more sudden than honest and constant. Her feelings towards the young sailor must have been equally favourable, one may suppose, as they often met at Penberth and elsewhere, and proposed to be wedded on his next return from a short voyage. But the artless sailor and simple maiden made their calculations without his parents' consent.

Little thought Mary, and less cared her lover, about what the old Pendars styled the stain on her paternity, or their talk about disowning or disinheriting. The brave heart of oak but little regarded his mother railing in bitter terms of Mary's poverty and base birth, and of Beaton's youthful failing; or his father saying, 'that as he made his bed he might lie on it; that if he wedded one of nought, he should be cut off with a shilling.'

But more deviltry was at work than the youngster knew of.

At parting, to join his ship, he told his father to keep his shilling, as he cared not for anything he had to withhold or bestow, that he saw no reason why the daughter should suffer for her parents' failings; he thought they had undergone more than enough themselves, and that he was determined to win fortune and to choose a wife for himself. On taking leave of Mary he assured her that when he returned from a short voyage he would make her his bride.

Pendar left home to join his ship. Many months elapsed, but Mary had no tidings of her affianced lover; and about the time she expected his return, a report was circulated that he was killed in a naval engagement. As months rolled on and brought no other intelligence, Mary too readily believed the common talk; and, poor grieved soul, for many an hour she would sit all alone on a rock beside the shore, look wistfully out to sea, and chant some old Breton melody about meeting her true love in the fairy orchards of Avalon. Like a blasted flower she pined and died, and was laid beside her parents, when the young seaman, her lover, was hastening homeward in hopes to make her his bride.

Pendar arrived at Penberth with a good store of prize-money, heard with anguish how Mary had died of a broken heart, all through a vile scheme of his parents, who had spread the sad rumour and had no reason to think him dead. Unknown to him they had contrived to have him drafted to a cruiser that was sent to protect merchantmen in distant seas. He was kept in ignorance of his destination and had no means to inform Mary that years might elapse before his return. He left home again without meeting his father or mother and never more returned to Buryan; yet 'tis said that he became renowned as a brave naval commander, and died unmarried.

Within a few days of Mary's death, her uncle made a trip to Fowey, with a cargo of contraband goods, and on his return voyage shaped his course for the Land's End, intending to land in Mount's Bay, to visit his niece and to persuade her to return with him. His ship approached land off Penberth; the sea being smooth he ran her close in, near the Cove, that he might be taken ashore in the ship's boat. It so happened that his old craft the *Mur* was running for the cove in this Autumn evening's twilight with a thick fog. The *Mur's* crew mistook I'an's vessel for a Revenue cutter, and one of the hands fired a random shot that killed their former commander as he was about to step into his boat. Some say it was the very evening of his niece's funeral. The Breton crew fired on the *Mur*, and sank her. Almost all Penberth men were on board, and the greatest part of them were drowned within hail of the cove and their dwellings. I'an was taken home to be buried in Brittany, and his family dropped all intercourse with their native place.

Fairies on Eastern Green

This story was told by the landlord of the inn at Zennor, some time around the 1860s:

There is some hope that all the fairy folk have not yet forsaken the neighbourhood of Penzance, as there are persons now living who have seen them dancing and holding their revels on the Eastern Green within the last fifty years. At that time, however, there were many acres of grass-grown sandy banks there, and a broad belt of soft green-sward, which skirted the carriage road, afforded a pleasant walk from Chyandour to Market-jew bridge. Great part of this Green has now been swept away by the waves.

The following fairy adventure was told me a short time since by a grave elderly man who heard it related by the principal person concerned in it, Tom Warren of Paul.

Tom Warren was noted as one of the boldest smugglers round. On a summer's night about forty years ago, he and five other men landed a boat-load of smuggled goods at a short distance from Long Rock. The brandy and other items having been taken above the high water mark, two of the men left for Market-jew, where their best customers lived, and one went over to Newtown to procure horses, so that the goods might be secured before daybreak.

Tom and the other two, being very tired, lay down by a heap of goods, hoping to get a doze while their comrades were away. They were soon disturbed, however, by the shrill tweeting of feapers [slit quills or reeds]. Besides, there was a constant tinkling, just like old women make by rattling pewter plates or brass pans to frighten their swarming bees home, or to make them settle.

The men thought this noise might be from a company of young folks keeping up a dance on the Green till a very late hour. Tom went to see who they were and to send them home, for it wasn't desirable for everybody to pry into the fair trader's business. Having passed the beach, he mounted a high sandbank to have a look round, as the music seemed very near him.

At a little distance, in hollows between sandbanks, he saw glimmering lights and persons like gaily dressed dolls skipping about and whirling round. Going nearer, he beheld, perched on a pretty high bank in their midst, a score or so of little odd-looking chaps; many of them blew in pan-pipes; some beat cymbals or tambourines, whilst others played on jew's harps or tweated on May whistles and feapers.

Tom noticed that the little men were rigged all in green, except their scarlet caps (small people are so fond of that coloured headgear that they used to be nick-named 'red-caps'.) But what struck him and tickled his fancy most was to see the little, old, grave-looking pipers with their long beards wagging.

In moving their mouths over the reeds, stuck in their breasts, they looked more like buck goats than anything human, so Tom said; and for the life of him he couldn't forebear shouting, 'Will 'e be shaved? Will 'e be shaved, old red-caps?'

He hailed them twice, and was about to do so again when all the dancers, with scores and hundreds more than he had noticed at first, sprang up, ranged themselves in rank and file; armed themselves in an instant with bows and arrows, spears and slings; then faced about, looking like vengeance. The band played a quick march and the troops of spriggans stamped on towards Tom, who saw them getting taller as they approached him. Their threatening looks were so frightful that he turned tail and ran down to his comrades and roused them, saying, 'Put to sea for your lives! There's thousands of small people and bucca-boos 'most on our backs! They'll soon surround us!'

Tom made off to the boat and his comrades followed hard at his heels; but on the way a shower of pebbles fell on them, 'and burned like coals o' fire wherever they hit them'.

The men pulled many fathoms from shore before they ventured to look up, though they knew themselves safe when on the sea, because none of the fairy tribe dare touch salt water.

At length, casting a glance landward, they saw ranged along the shore a company of as ugly looking creatures as they ever beheld, making threatening gestures and vain attempts to throw stones at them. When a furlong or so from land the men rested on their oars and kept watching their assailants till near daybreak. Then horses were heard galloping along the road from Market-jew: the small people retreated to the sandbanks and the smugglers rowed to land. Tom again shouted to the retiring host, 'We'll shave 'e all and cut your tails off, ef you ever show here any more.' But the fairies disdained to notice his impudence and presently disappeared.

The other smugglers, who were now on the beach with plenty of help, on seeing their mates leaving the boat enquired if the riding officer had hove in sight. In such a case smugglers usually took to sea that they might not be recognised; they didn't mind his seeing the goods, for the most valuable would be secured before the king's men came to take them.

After spileing an anker [tapping a keg] and treating all the neighbours who came to help or purchase or both, Tom related how they had to run for their lives and take to sea in order to escape an army of small people. Some could scarcely believe it, though others thought the story likely enough. All blamed Tom for mocking the fairies, and said bad luck would cross his path, ere long, for that night's work. Aye, and their forebodings were verified before another summer came round. However, without further mishap for that night the goods were quickly disposed of – the greater part in Market-jew, and the rest left in an old tin work near the Marsh, till wanted.

'There never was a better pare [company] of fair traders than Tom and his mates,' continued the landlord, 'and they found good customers in the old well-to-do farmers of Zennor, who dearly loved their toddy, the Lord rest them.'

The mermaid of Zennor

Hundreds of years ago a very beautiful and richly attired lady attended services in Zennor Church occasionally – now and then she went to Morvah also. Her visits were by no means regular and often long intervals would elapse between them.

Yet whenever she came the people were enchanted with her good looks and sweet singing. Although Zennor folks were remarkable for fine psalmody, she excelled them all and they wondered how, after the scores of years that they had seen her, she continued to look so young and fair. No one knew whence she came, nor whither she went, yet many watched her as far as they could see from Tregarthen Hill.

She took some notice of a fine young man, called Matthey Trewella, who was the best singer in the parish. He once followed her, but he never returned; after that she was never more seen in Zennor Church, and it might not have been known to this day who or what she was but for the merest accident.

One Sunday morning a vessel cast anchor about a mile from Pendower Cove; soon after, a mermaid came alongside and hailed the ship. Rising out of the water as far as her waist, with her yellow hair floating around her, she told the captain that she was returning from church, and requested him to trip his anchor just for a minute, as the fluke of it rested on the door of her dwelling, and she was anxious to get in to her children.

Others say that while she was out on the ocean a-fishing of a Sunday morning, the anchor was dropped on the trap-door which gave access to her submarine abode. Finding on her return how she was hindered from opening her door, she begged the captain to have the anchor raised that she might enter her dwelling to dress her children and be ready in time for church. However it may have been, her polite request had a magical effect on the sailors, for they immediately worked with a will, hove anchor and set sail, not wishing to remain a moment longer than they could help near her habitation. Seafaring men, who understood most about mermaids, regarded their appearance as a token that bad luck was at hand. It was believed they could take such shapes as suited their purpose, and that they had often allured men to live with them.

When Zennor folks learnt that a mermaid dwelt near Pendower, and what she had told the captain, they concluded it was this sea-lady who had visited their church and enticed Trewella to her abode. To commemorate these somewhat unusual events they had the figure she bore – when in her ocean home – carved in holy oak, which may still be seen.

The Queen's visit to Baranhual

There is a tradition in Buryan that when the Pendars lived in grand style in Baranhual, a queen and her retinue landed from a man-of-war at Mousal, for the sake of seeing the Logan Rock and Land's End. News of the intended trip soon spread, and reached Buryan ere sufficient horses could be procured to furnish out the cavalcade. On the morning of the royal progress, work was at a standstill and nearly all who could 'lift a leg' started off from house and field towards Buryan Church-town, as it was rumoured that Her Majesty intended to inspect Buryan church on her way. So, in the morning early, Buryan bells were set a-ringing and Church-town folks arrayed themselves in their best to receive the Queen with due honours.

Every soul left Baranhual except old Dame Pendar, who was rather infirm. 'My Lady the Queen,' said she, 'is but a woman, and make the most of her, even if she do wear a crown on her head every day of her life, with velvet robes all 'broidered in gold, silk stockings and diamond buckles on her satin shoes, with rings on her fingers and bells on her toes, yet she's much like myself under all her fine clothes; and it esn't worth while to leave the house alone, and all that's in it, and go so far to see her at my time of life. Besides, there's the milk to scald and many jobs to be done at all hours. No, verily,' said she to her son and his wife, 'you may be off to Church-town with the scabble-an-gow, but indeed I'll stay home and guard the house, and all that's in it. That shall never be left alone whilst I draw breath.'

At that time the Pendars kept a capstan in repair and gave other aid to the fishery at Penberth – which is partly in Baranhual ground – and received for it a certain portion of fish from the owners of each boat kept in the cove.

An hour or so after all the household, except old mistress, had started off to behold a queen, An' Joan Taskes came up from Penberth with a cowal [tub] full of fish, as the squire's dues from all the boats which landed that morning. Madam told An' Joan to take the fish to the river, and that she would be down in a minute to help clean them. Before Joan had taken all out of her cowal and laid them on the stepping stones, that stood in the water where Baranhual bridge now crosses it, old mistress arrived knife in hand, ready to help clean and split her fish. They had nearly finished their job – the old lady standing on a stepping stone with her skirts tucked up to her knees, taking the fish from An' Joan, who waded in the stream to give them a last rinsing – when the old fish-wife, on hearing the clatter of a horse's hoofs coming down hill, looked up, turned round and bawled out, 'Can I believe my eyes? Look 'e, mistress dear, ef I live, there's hundreds of kings and queens ridan down the hill. I can see more than a score, and there's more a-coman round the turnan; pull down your petticoats, do! Oh, I wish to gracious I had a clean towser [apron] on, and my best hat!'

Before old Joan had finished exclaiming, and fixing herself as tidy as she could – though Madam Pendar, intent on the fish, didn't notice her commotion – a score or so of ladies and gentlemen on horseback were within a stone's cast. They drew rein, and a horseman started forward, rode down into the water, accosted the old lady, enquired if

Squire Pendar lived in the house on the hill, and informed the wondering woman that Her Majesty on her route to the Logan Rock, well remembering that the Pendars had always been stout friends to the royal cause, had preferred coming that way to give him a visit, rather than seeing Buryan Church, which Her Majesty and her attendants might have a glance at on their return from the Land's End. Madam replied that she was very glad to see 'my lady, the Queen'; and was sorry that her son and his wife with all their servants were gone to pay their respects to Her Majesty in Church-town, as everybody said that was the intended route, and nobody but herself to receive them.

'My royal mistress approaches to speak for herself,' said he.

Madam was still standing on a stone, knife in hand, her coats tucked up and kirtle drawn through her apron string, when the Queen, understanding that her gentleman was speaking to no less a person than Madam Pendar, rode into the water, shook hands with her and said, 'If all are gone to see the Queen and left 'e alone, the Queen is come to see you; and I and my attendants would be glad to rest a while to have something to eat, and to mend the rents in our clothes that are torn to skethans with thorns and brambles that overhang the narrow lanes.'

'The Lord love 'e, my dear lady the Queen,' exclaimed she, making a low curtsey and quite overcome with honour. 'Do 'e put your hand, now – as mine on that side is fishy and wet – into my left pocket, take out the key of the fore-door, and my huzzey. You will find in it needles and thread of all colours. Ride up to the house, let yourselves in, and I'll follow with the fish, and do the best we can to entertain 'e.'

'We should like nothing so much as some of that nice fish, draining on the stones,' said the Queen, trying to get a key, large enough for a church door, out of Madam's pocket.

'Bless your life, and you shall have them,' replied the old lady. 'I am so flambustered with the honour you have done me, that I hardly know which end I stand upon. But you will want my scissors, pieces of stuff, and other things in my pockets, for mending,' she continued, untying the string from around her waist, that kept up her pockets. 'Take them all as they are; you will find most everything in them.'

The precious pockets, like knapsacks, were handed to a gentleman who slung them across his saddle-bow, and the Queen rode on well pleased with Dame Pendar.

Joan stood gaping and staring, nodding and smiling, without speaking a word, though many spoke to her. But their backs were no sooner turned than she said, 'Why mistress dear, can you make out their lingo? Can that lady, who spoke to 'e, be a Queen? Why, where's her crown? It wasn't upon her head, I'm sure.'

'Cease thy clack, be quick and gather up the fish,' Madam replied. 'She put her crown in her pocket, I suppose, that the thorns mightn't sweep it off her head and under the horses' feet; thee west see her wearing of it when she's seated in the great parlour, by and by, eating bread and honey. I am glad, though, thee hast brought up a lot of nice mullet, bass, whiting-pullocks, and other fish for pies and frying, besides good large cod and ling for boiling.'

When Dame Pendar and Joan got up to the house, they found the Queen and her ladies in the parlour busy sewing up rents in their garments, and the gentlemen – having stabled their horses – had made a blazing fire on the hearth. A large brass brewing pan was placed on a brandes [trivet], pounds of butter and lard cast into it, and the nicest frying fish cooked therein.

Mullet and parsley pies were put to bake on the hearth, large fishes boiled and congers stewed with fennel, in as many crocks and kettles as it would contain, with other things. Ladies and gentlemen – Queen and all – helped: some got the best pewter platters, plates and flagons, only used on grand occasions, out of a chest; those on dressers and shelves, for ordinary use, weren't half enough. Others peeled garlic and hollick [shallot], chopped fennel, tarragon and other herbs to flavour sauces. Several tried to grind mustard, but none could give the right motion to their knees to make the bullet spin round in the bowl, and the old mistress was obliged to grind it all, or have it spoiled. They dished up fried and boiled fish, swimming in butter; bowls of cream were poured into the pies; lucky too, Madam had a batch of barley bread just baked, hot and hot.

Two gentlemen placed a high-backed carved oak chair, with several pillows thereon, at the head of the hall table, and Her Majesty was seated in as much state as she desired. They ate, one and all, with such an appetite as if they hadn't tasted meat for a week, so old Joan Taskes said after. The Queen imbibed old ale from a silver goblet; her ladies from pewter tankards and flagons; her gentlemen drank beer and cider from black-jacks and brown georges [leather drinking vessels], which were often replenished.

Wasn't Dame Pendar delighted to see it all, as she bustled about to help Her Majesty to all kinds of sauces, of her own compounding. Indeed it was, as she said, the proudest day of her life. She was above all elated when her royal guest smacked her lips after a sip of brandy, and swore 'by cock and pie' that 'true as she was a sinner, never before in all her born days had she so much enjoyed a repast.'

When the Queen and her ladies returned to the parlour, Dame

Pendar placed before them white bread, cream and honey, brandy, sweet drink [mead] and other cordials, of which they all partook with great pleasure. Having mended their garments, the ladies thought it full time to proceed on their journey, if they were to see the Land's End and Logan Rock that day.

But Her Majesty, bless her honest heart, was so well pleased with her entertainment that she preferred to stay there with old Dame Pendar till her attendants returned; so they, with her permission, rode away to Castle Treen.

When the Queen's suite had departed, Dame Pendar produced from her own private cupboard a bottle of rare old mead, and a flask of extra strong brandy, for Her Majesty to taste; and she, liking them well, drank glass upon glass of mead, with several sips of brandy, to keep the fish from 'flowing on her stomach'; and to show their loving regard for each other, they exchanged all the contents of their pockets for keepsakes, yea, every item – except their crooked sixpences which they kept for good luck.

At length the Queen, feeling drowsy, reclined in a long window-seat, thence rolled on the floor, where she lay puffing and snoring, unable to rise. Dame Pendar, by so often drinking 'Here's health and long life to 'e, my dear lady, the Queen,' was too fuddled to help her up, so she lay down with her for company. Old Joan, who had been sipping of all sorts, and drinking everybody's health, was stretched under the kitchen table.

The Queen's attendants, having passed hours in viewing Logan Rock and the other wonders of Castle Treen, couranted about amongst the rocks, where they found pleasant places for courting, till nearly sunset. Then, concluding it was too late for going to the Land's End, they mounted and returned to Baranhual that they might wait on their royal mistress, and reach Mousal in time to be on board before dark. They galloped away in hot haste, expecting to find Her Majesty impatiently awaiting their return; but, sad to say, they found her – all her state forgotten – lying helpless on the floor beside Dame Pendar. The royal lady was hastily lifted on her palfrey. Joan Taskes – now the least drunk of the three – helped to fasten a girth across her Majesty's lap, to keep her safe in the saddle, and they quickly departed.

Now it so happened that Squire Pendar, his wife and their servants, tired of waiting for the Queen in Churchtown till near night, returned home across the fields Selena way and arrived at the Green-court gate just in time for him to catch a glimpse of Her Majesty under the trees that darkened the avenue. He had the merest glance of her going down the hill with her head drooping over her horse's mane, and a gentleman holding her steady. And that was the last seen of her in Buryan. Squire Pendar, his wife and their servants were all rather muddled too, from having spent the day in Churchtown with hundreds of gentle and simple, all drinking, 'Here's to the Queen and ourselves, comrades!' Yet he and his wife expressed great surprise and ill-humour at finding their house all in disorder.

Joan told them how they had all enjoyed their entertainment. 'Bad luck to them all!' murmured he; 'Our cellar floor is like mud with spilt liquor, and not a gallon of beer or cider left in the casks. What mother said was true enough: the Queen, for all her fine clothes, is much like another woman, especially when drunk.' Next morning he could hardly be persuaded that Her Majesty had been there at all, till his mother showed him what fine things she had kept as keepsakes. 'My thimble, as thou knowest, was brass,' she said, 'and my bodkin silver; but see, here's my gracious lady's silver thimble and gold bodkin.' Then, with great pride, drawing from her pocket the Queen's huzzey, she continued, 'If anything more is wanted to assure thee how I've been honoured by my gracious lady, behold this!' She then displayed a remarkable contrivance for containing many requisites of a lady's work-box, and several toilet articles besides. It was a yard long when unfolded; every little pocket and flap of a different sort of rich stuff, all worked in elegant designs with gold and silver thread, coloured silks intermixed with pearls and precious stones, or what passed for such. It folded into strong leather covers, fastened with silver clasps like a book, and the upper cover was lined with a mirror.

Hundreds of people came to see it, suspended at full length, the looking glass at the top, over the parlour fire-place, where it was kept in remembrance of the Queen's visit.

We have frequently remarked to old persons who related this story, that nothing is said in any county or other history about a Queen ever having visited Baranhual. 'Perhaps your history makers never heard of it,' they reply. 'No one belonging to Buryan saw her plainly, that's true, except the two old women.'

Squire Pendar and his servants only had a glimpse in the twilight of a company on horseback passing down the road, then overhung with large spreading sycamores which soon hid his royal guests. But the Pendars, even in our own time, poor as they were – many of them labourers and fishermen – had always preserved something among them that the Queen was said to have left with old Madam hundreds of years ago; and all of the name, that we have met with, say that Pendre, Baranhual, Trevider and other lands in Buryan once belonged to their forefathers.